LEARNING TO READ:
NEW TESTAMENT STORIES

Printed in the United States of America

First Printing, 2017

ISBN: 978-0-9985228-0-7 (print)
ISBN: 978-0-9985228-2-1 (ebook)

"Hear the instruction of thy father, and forsake not the law of thy mother."
Proverbs 1:8

Acknowledgements

I would like to first thank my husband, Don, who is an inspiration and support in everything I do. My children, David and Joseph, give me hope to believe in all that is good. I would also like to thank my parents, Marian and Bernard Sheptoski, for teaching me to love the word of God.

Preface

<u>Learning to Read: New Testament Stories</u> teaches children to love reading while learning about God. Reading becomes fun. The basal reading approach is an easy way to learn how to read.

For those who want to learn more, <u>Learning to Read: New Testament Stories Study Guide</u> completes the reading development process.

It's a good idea for parents to preview a book before their child reads it.

Contents

Acknowledgements v
Preface vii

Jesus 1
The Wise Men 2
The Boy Jesus 3
Jesus is Baptized 4
Jesus is Tempted 5
Jesus in the Temple 6
Jesus Chooses His Apostles 7
The Man Who Walked 8
The Sermon on the Mount 9
Prayer 10
Jesus Feeds 5,000 People 11
Jesus Walks on the Water 12
Jesus Heals a Blind Man 13
The Good Samaritan 14
The Lost Son 15
The Ten Lepers 16
The Little Children 17
Eternal Life 18
The Widow's Mites 19
The Ten Young Women 20
The Talents 21
Lazarus 22
The Sacrament 23
The Garden of Gethsemane 24
Jesus is Crucified 25

Jesus is Resurrected.. 26

The Apostles.. 27

Peter Heals Tabitha 28

Paul.. 29

The Apostle John 30

Appendix A 31
    Directions – Reading Skills Development

List of Visuals 33

Jesus

1. An **angel** told Joseph that Mary was going to have a **baby.** He said the baby came from **God**.
2. Joseph **married** Mary.
3. Mary had a baby **boy**. She called him **Jesus**.
4. Jesus was **born** to **save** us from our **sins**.

(Matthew 2:1-11)

The Wise Men

1. The **wise men** wanted to **find** Jesus to **worship** him.
2. There was a new **star** in the **sky**.
3. It led them to Jesus in **Bethlehem**.
4. The wise men gave **gifts** to Jesus.

The Boy Jesus

1. Jesus and his **family** were in Jerusalem for the **Passover**.
2. Jesus was not with his family as they went **home**.
3. Joseph and Mary went back to **Jerusalem** to find Jesus.
4. Joseph and Mary saw Jesus **teaching** in the **temple**.
5. Jesus **left** with Joseph and Mary to go home.

Jesus is Baptized

1. John the Baptist **baptized people** in a **river**.
2. Jesus came to the river. He asked John to baptize him.
3. John asked Jesus why he wanted to be baptized.
4. Jesus said he wanted to **obey** God.
5. John baptized Jesus.
6. God was **happy** with Jesus.

(Matthew 4:1-11)

Jesus is Tempted

1. Jesus went to the **desert** to **fast** and **pray**.
2. The **devil** told Jesus to make **bread** to eat.
3. The devil told Jesus to fall down to **test** God.
4. The devil told Jesus to worship him.
5. Jesus did not do any of this.
6. Jesus told the devil to go **away**.

(John 2:13-16, Matthew 21:13)

Jesus in the Temple

1. Jesus saw people **selling animals** by **tables** in the temple.
2. Jesus told the people to not sell animals in the temple.
3. Jesus **overturned** the tables.
4. They left the temple.
5. Jesus said the temple is a **house** of prayer.

(Luke 5:1-11, Luke 6:13-14)

Jesus Chooses His Apostles

1. Peter had been **fishing** with James and John. They did not have any **fish**.
2. Jesus told Peter to **move** the **boat**.
3. Jesus told Peter to put the **nets** down in the **water**.
4. Many fish went in the nets.
5. Peter, James and John left their boats to be with Jesus.
6. Jesus **chose** them to be his **apostles**.

(Luke 5:18-25)

The Man Who Walked

1. Jesus was in a house teaching people.
2. A **man** who was **unable** to **walk** had **friends** take him on his **bed** to the house.
3. The friends let the man down from a **hole** in the **top** of the house to be by Jesus.
4. Jesus told the man to take up his bed and walk.
5. The man had **faith** in Jesus. He took up his bed and walked.

(Matthew 5:1-48)

The Sermon on the Mount

1. Jesus went up to a **mountain** to teach the people about God.
2. Jesus said the **humble** are **blessed**.
3. Jesus said to **help** people that are **sad** and you will be happier.
4. Jesus said to **forgive** your **enemies** to be forgiven.
5. Jesus said to be **good** to all people.
6. Jesus gave this **sermon** to the people.

(Matthew 6: 5-13, John 16:23)

Prayer

1. Jesus said a prayer to teach his **disciples** how to pray.
2. Jesus said to pray to **Heavenly Father**.
3. Jesus **thanked** God.
4. Jesus asked God for help.
5. Jesus said **amen**.
6. Jesus said to pray in his **name**.

(Matthew 14:13-21)

Jesus Feeds 5,000 People

1. Jesus told his disciples to **feed** all of the **5,000 hungry** people.
2. They **only** had five **loaves** of bread and two fish.
3. Jesus blessed the **food**.
4. The disciples **passed** the food to the people.
5. The people had **enough** food to eat.
6. This was a **miracle**.

(Matthew 14:22-33)

Jesus Walks on the Water

1. The disciples were on a boat.
2. Jesus walked on the water to them.
3. Jesus told Peter to come to him.
4. Peter walked on the water to Jesus.
5. Peter looked down at the **waves** and began to **sink**.
6. Jesus took Peter's **hand**.
7. Jesus told Peter to have **more** faith.

(John 9:1-38)

Jesus Heals a Blind Man

1. Jesus met a **blind** man.
2. Jesus made **clay**. He put clay on the **eyes** of the blind man.
3. Jesus told the blind man to **wash** in a **pool**.
4. The blind man washed in the pool and did see.
5. The man told **others** how Jesus had **healed** him.
6. The man worshipped Jesus.

(Luke 10:25-37)

The Good Samaritan

1. Jesus told a **story** to a **lawyer**.
2. A **priest** saw a man on the **road** was **hurt**. He did not help him.
3. A **worker** in the temple saw a man on the road was hurt. He did not help him.
4. A **Samaritan** saw a man on the road was hurt. The man was a **Jew**.
5. The Jews and Samaritans did not **like** each other.
6. The Samaritan helped the man.
7. Jesus said the Samaritan was a good **neighbor.**

(Luke 15:10-32)

The Lost Son

1. Jesus told a story about a man that had two **sons**.
2. The **younger** son took the **money** his **father** had for him and left home.
3. The younger son went back home when he used it all up.
4. The father gave a **party** for the younger son.
5. The **older** son asked why his father did this.
6. The father said he was happy the younger son was **sorry** for what he had done.

(Luke 17:12-19)

The Ten Lepers

1. Ten **lepers** asked Jesus to heal them.
2. Jesus told the lepers to find a priest and show him that they were **clean**.
3. The lepers did what Jesus told them to do.
4. All of the ten lepers were healed.
5. One of the ten lepers thanked Jesus.
6. Jesus said the leper's faith had helped heal him.

(Mark 10:13-16)

The Little Children

1. The people took their **little children** to Jesus.
2. The disciples told the people to not **bring** their children to Jesus.
3. Jesus wanted the little children to come to him.
4. Jesus said little children **belong** to the **kingdom** of God.
5. Jesus told the people to become like little children.
6. Jesus blessed the little children.

(Mark 10:17-30)

Eternal Life

1. A **rich** young man asked Jesus what he needed to do to have **eternal life**.
2. Jesus told the young man to obey the **commandments**.
3. The young man said he did.
4. Jesus told the young man to give all that he had to the **poor**.
5. The young man did not do this.
6. Jesus said it is not **easy** for a rich man to give all to God.

(Mark 12:41-44)

The Widow's Mites

1. Jesus told his disciples a story about a **widow**.
2. The rich men gave a lot of money to the **church**.
3. The rich men had money at home.
4. A widow gave two **mites** to the church.
5. She did not have money at home.
6. Jesus said the widow **sacrificed** more than the rich men.

(Matthew 25:1-13)

The Ten Young Women

1. Jesus told a story about ten young **women** that went to a **wedding**.
2. They **waited** by the **door** with their **lamps**.
3. The five wise young women had **oil** in their lamps.
4. When the door was **open** they went **inside**.
5. The other five young women had gone to **buy** oil for their lamps.
6. Jesus said he wants us to be like the five wise young women.

(Matthew 25:14-30)

The Talents

1. Jesus told a story about a man that gave three people some **talents**.
2. Two people worked to have more talents.
3. The man was happy with them.
4. The **last** person did not work. He did not have more talents.
5. The man took his talent away from him. He gave it to one that had more talents.
6. Jesus said we need to do our **best** for the kingdom of God.

Lazarus

1. The **sisters** of Lazarus asked Jesus to heal him.
2. Jesus was away when Lazarus **died**.
3. Lazarus was **buried** in a **cave** when Jesus came to him.
4. Jesus told Lazarus to come out of the cave.
5. Lazarus was **alive again**. He sat up and walked out of the cave.

(Luke 22:7-20, Matthew 26:26-27)

The Sacrament

1. Jesus and his apostles met **together** in a **room**.
2. Jesus blessed the bread. He **broke** it into **pieces**.
3. Jesus **poured wine** into a cup and blessed it.
4. They ate the bread and **drank** the wine.
5. The **sacrament** was given to help them **remember** Jesus.

(Matthew 26:36-44, Luke 22:42, 44)

The Garden of Gethsemane

1. Jesus and his apostles went to the **Garden** of **Gethsemane**.
2. Peter, James and John went with Jesus to find a place to pray.
3. Jesus prayed to God.
4. The apostles went to **sleep**.
5. Jesus **woke** them up to pray.
6. Jesus took on **himself** our sins.

(Luke 23:1-46, John 19:23)

Jesus is Crucified

1. Jesus was taken to the **governor** Pilate.
2. Pilate let the people tell him what to do.
3. The people did not want Jesus to live.
4. Pilate told his **soldiers** to put Jesus on a **cross**.
5. Jesus asked God to forgive the people.
6. Jesus was **crucified**.

(John 20:1-17)

Jesus is Resurrected

1. Jesus had been buried for three days.
2. Mary Magdalene went to see Jesus.
3. Jesus was not in the **tomb**.
4. Mary Magdalene began to **cry**.
5. A man **behind** her asked her why she was crying.
6. It was Jesus who was **resurrected**.

(John 21:14-17, Acts 1:8)

The Apostles

1. The apostles ate with the resurrected Jesus.
2. Jesus asked Peter if he **loved** him.
3. Peter said he did.
4. Jesus said to **share** the **gospel**.
5. Jesus told the apostles to be **witnesses** of him.

Peter Heals Tabitha

1. Tabitha did many good **deeds**.
2. One day she died.
3. Tabitha's friends asked Peter to heal her.
4. Peter prayed to God.
5. Peter told Tabitha to get up.
6. Tabitha was alive again.

(Acts 9:1-18, 26:14-25)

Paul

1. Paul saw a **bright light** from **heaven**.
2. A **voice** told Paul to sin no more.
3. Paul became blind.
4. Paul met Ananias who gave him a **blessing**.
5. Paul was no **longer** blind.
6. Paul was baptized and became a **missionary**.

(Revelation 1:1-11, 16:16, 20:12, 21:7)

The Apostle John

1. The apostle John had a **revelation**.
2. John saw Jesus come to **earth** again.
3. John saw the **wicked** at **war** with the **saints**.
4. John saw God **judge** all people.
5. John said the **righteous** will live with God.

Appendix A

Directions – Reading Skills Development

Instructions: Read to your child. Instruct your child to read each story out loud and silently. The words in **bold** are the new words your child will be learning in the story.

<u>Story Text</u>

1. An **angel** told Joseph that Mary was going to have a **baby.** He said the baby came from **God**.

The new vocabulary words are angel, baby and God.

List of Visuals

Jesus: Distant Shores Media/Sweet Publishing, CC BY-SA 3.0, https://commons.wikimedia.org/w/index.php?curid=18887032

The Wise Men: Distant Shores Media/Sweet Publishing, CC BY-SA 3.0, https://commons.wikimedia.org/w/index.php?curid=18885211

The Boy Jesus: Distant Shores Media/Sweet Publishing, CC BY-SA 3.0, https://commons.wikimedia.org/w/index.php?curid=18887083

Jesus is Baptized: Distant Shores Media/Sweet Publishing, CC BY-SA 3.0, https://commons.wikimedia.org/w/index.php?curid=18888303

Jesus is Tempted: Distant Shores Media/Sweet Publishing, CC BY-SA 3.0, https://commons.wikimedia.org/w/index.php?curid=18885299

Jesus in the Temple: Distant Shores Media/Sweet Publishing, CC BY-SA 3.0, https://commons.wikimedia.org/w/index.php?curid=18887851

Jesus Chooses His Apostles: Distant Shores Media/Sweet Publishing, CC BY-SA 3.0, https://commons.wikimedia.org/w/index.php?curid=18887308

The Man Who Walked: Distant Shores Media/Sweet Publishing, CC BY-SA 3.0, https://commons.wikimedia.org/w/index.php?curid=18887253

The Sermon on the Mount: Distant Shores Media/Sweet Publishing, CC BY-SA 3.0, https://commons.wikimedia.org/w/index.php?curid=18887341

The Talents: Distant Shores Media/Sweet Publishing, CC BY-SA 3.0,
https://commons.wikimedia.org/w/index.php?curid=18885730

Lazarus: Distant Shores Media/Sweet Publishing, CC BY-SA 3.0,
https://commons.wikimedia.org/w/index.php?curid=18888571

The Sacrament: Distant Shores Media/Sweet Publishing, CC BY-SA 3.0,
https://commons.wikimedia.org/w/index.php?curid=18888057

The Garden of Gethsemane: Distant Shores Media/Sweet Publishing, CC BY-SA 3.0,
https://commons.wikimedia.org/w/index.php?curid=18886817

Jesus is Crucified: Distant Shores Media/Sweet Publishing, CC BY-SA 3.0,
https://commons.wikimedia.org/w/index.php?curid=18888154

Jesus is Resurrected: Distant Shores Media/Sweet Publishing, CC BY-SA 3.0,
https://commons.wikimedia.org/w/index.php?curid=18888195

The Apostles: Distant Shores Media/Sweet Publishing, CC BY-SA 3.0,
https://commons.wikimedia.org/w/index.php?curid=18888825

Peter Heals Tabitha: Distant Shores Media/Sweet Publishing, CC BY-SA 3.0,
https://commons.wikimedia.org/w/index.php?curid=18889202

Paul: Distant Shores Media/Sweet Publishing, CC BY-SA 3.0,
https://commons.wikimedia.org/w/index.php?curid=18889115

The Apostle John: Distant Shores Media/Sweet Publishing, CC BY-SA 3.0,
https://commons.wikimedia.org/w/index.php?curid=18753660

Made in the USA
Columbia, SC
21 September 2018